W9-ARL-684

FACE TO Face

EDITED BY LARRY CARRIER

COVER DESIGN BY JON KOPP

SOUNDFORTH

© 2002 SoundForth. Greenville, South Carolina 29614.
All rights reserved.

Contents

O Come and Sing unto the Lord

Based on Psalm 95, from *The Psalter*, 1912, alt.

Lloyd Larson (ASCAP)

*An orchestral accompaniment CD is available for this song. Please call 1-800-258-7288.

© 2000, 2002 by SoundForth®, Greenville, SC 29614. All rights reserved. Printed in the U.S.A.
Duplication in any form prohibited without written permission from the publisher.

joy - ful songs the Lord,____ our Sav - ior, praise! Be -

fore God's pres - ence let us come with praise and thank - ful

voice;_____ Let us sing psalms to God____ with grace, with

grate - ful hearts____ re - joice. O

Lord our God is King____ of kings, a - bove____ all gods en -

throned;_____ the depths of earth and moun - tains high by

God____ a - lone____ are owned._____ To God the spa - cious

sea be - longs; God made its waves and tides._____ And

by God's hand the ris - ing land was

formed,_____ and still_____ a - bides.

O come, and bow - ing down to God, our

wor - ship let us bring;_____ Come, let us kneel be -

By the Grace of God

Reece Yandle

Reece Yandle
Arranged by Jenifer Cook

© 2002 by SoundForth®, Greenville, SC 29614. All rights reserved. Printed in the U.S.A.
Duplication in any form prohibited without written permission from the publisher.

Face to Face

Carrie E. Breck

Alexander Kruchkov

*An orchestral accompaniment CD is available for this song. Please call 1-800-258-7288.

© 2002 by SoundForth®, Greenville, SC 29614. All rights reserved. Printed in the U.S.A.
Duplication in any form prohibited without written permission from the publisher.

be—

When with rap-ture I be-hold___ Him, Je-sus

Voice I *mp*

On-ly faint-ly now I

Christ who died for me?

see___ Him, With a dark - 'ning veil be-tween,

What re - joic - ing in His pres - ence, When are ban - ished grief and

pain; When the crook - ed ways are straight - ened, And the

dark things shall be plain.

Face to face— O bliss - ful

for Angela Huffstutler

My Heart Now Sings

John Mason

Sandra Achterberg

Slowly, devotionally ♩ = 84

I've found the pearl of great-est price, My heart now sings___ for___ joy; And praise I must, for Christ is mine, Christ___ shall my song em-

© 2002 by SoundForth®, Greenville, SC 29614. All rights reserved. Printed in the U.S.A.
Duplication in any form prohibited without written permission from the publisher.

23

Jesus, I Am Resting, Resting

Jean S. Pigott

Ruth Coleman

+Individual trombone part may be found on page 117.

*An orchestral accompaniment CD is available for this song. Please call 1-800-258-7288.

© 2002 by SoundForth®, Greenville, SC 29614. All rights reserved. Printed in the U.S.A.
Duplication in any form prohibited without written permission from the publisher.

heart. Thou hast bid me gaze up-on Thee, And Thy beau-ty

fills my soul, For by Thy trans-form-ing pow-er, Thou hast made me

whole.

Simply trusting Thee, Lord Jesus, I behold Thee as Thou art, And Thy love, so pure, so changeless, Satisfies my heart, Satisfies its deepest longings, Meets, supplies its

every need, Com - pass - eth me round with bless - ings: Thine is love in-

deed!

Ev - er lift Thy face up - on me As I work and wait for Thee;

Rest - ing 'neath Thy smile, Lord Je - sus, Earth's dark shad - ows

flee. Bright - ness of my Fa - ther's glo - ry, Sun - shine of my

Complete in Thee

Aaron R. Wolfe
Refrain, James M. Gray

Talmadge J. Bittikofer
Arranged by Alexander Kruchkov

+Individual flute parts may be found on pages 119 and 121.

© 2002 by SoundForth®, Greenville, SC 29614. All rights reserved. Printed in the U.S.A.
Duplication in any form prohibited without written permission from the publisher.

V. I
Yea, just - ti - fied! O bless - ed thought! And sanc - ti -

V. II
Yea, just - ti - fied! O bless - ed thought! And sanc - ti -

V. I
fied! Sal - va - tion wrought! Thy blood hath par - don bought for

V. II
fied! Sal - va - tion wrought! Thy blood hath par - don bought for

V. I
me, And glo - ri - fied, I, too, shall be!

V. II
me, And glo - ri - fied, I, too, shall be!

be, I ask no more, com-plete in Thee.

Hark, the Voice of Jesus Calling

Daniel March, alt.

Phillip Landgrave

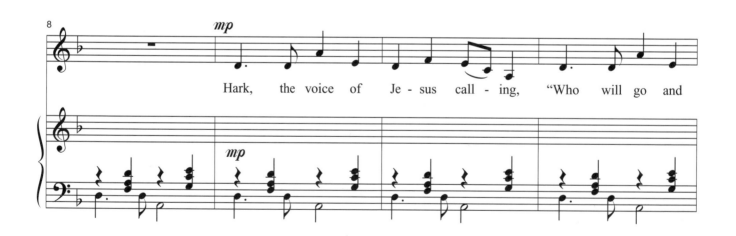

Hark, the voice of Je - sus call - ing, "Who will go and

© *Copyright 1968, Broadman Press. All rights reserved. International copyright secured. Used by permission.*

If you can-not cross the o-cean And the hea-then lands ex - plore, You can find the hea-then near - er; You can help them at your__ door: If you can-not give your thou - sands, You can give the wid - ow's__ mite; What you tru - ly give for Je - sus Will be pre - cious

in His____ sight.____

Let none hear you i - dly say - ing, "There is noth - ing I can__ do."

While the souls of men are dy - ing, And the Mas - ter calls for__ you;

Take the task he gives you glad - ly; Let His work your plea - sure be;

for Dawn Braun

Precious Blood of Jesus

Frances R. Havergal

Sandra H. Achterberg

© *2002 by SoundForth®, Greenville, SC 29614. All rights reserved. Printed in the U.S.A.*
Duplication in any form prohibited without written permission from the publisher.

Take Me, Lord

Roma J. Schankweiler

Roma J. Schankweiler
Arranged by Karen Kuehmann

*An orchestral accompaniment CD is available for this song. Please call 1-800-258-7288.

© 2002 by SoundForth®, Greenville, SC 29614. All rights reserved. Printed in the U.S.A.
Duplication in any form prohibited without written permission from the publisher.

Light of the World

Diane L. Parsons Bugg

Diane L. Parsons Bugg

Light of the world, il - lu - mine me.

Thou hast the truth that sets cap - tives free.

True light is found in Thee a - lone.

© 2001, 2002 by SoundForth®, Greenville, SC 29614. All rights reserved. Printed in the U.S.A.
Duplication in any form prohibited without written permission from the publisher.

treat. Light of the world, il - lu - mine me. No light on earth can com - pare with Thee. Thine are the moon, the stars, the sun. Re - flect through me, O Thou Ho - ly

Take all my pas - sion, will, and pride,

That I may love Thee, in Thee a - bide.

Light of the world. Light of the world._____

_____ Thy Word is a lamp un - to my

He Maketh No Mistake

A. M. Overton

Megan McCauley

Gently and with confidence ♩ = 72-80

Piano

mf

Solo *mf*

My__ Fath- er's way may twist and turn, My

heart may throb and ache, But__ in my soul I'm

L.H.

© 2002 by SoundForth®, Greenville, SC 29614. All rights reserved. Printed in the U.S.A.
Duplication in any form prohibited without written permission from the publisher.

My cher-ished plans may go a-stray, My hopes may fade a-way, But still I'll trust the Lord to lead, For He doth know the way. Though night be dark and it may seem that day will nev-er

Guide Me Day by Day

Joyce Snyder

Roma J. Schankweiler and Alexander Kruchkov
Arranged by Alexander Kruchkov

© 2002 by SoundForth®, Greenville, SC 29614. All rights reserved. Printed in the U.S.A.
Duplication in any form prohibited without written permission from the publisher.

72

O Sav - ior, guide my foot-steps, and light my path, I

O Sav - ior, guide my foot-steps, and light my path, I___

pray. Help me, Lord, to live for Thee, and guide me day by

pray. and guide me day by

day. In

day.

74

for Brian and Heidi

Wedding Prayer

Frederick William Foster
and Sandra Achterberg

Sandra Achterberg

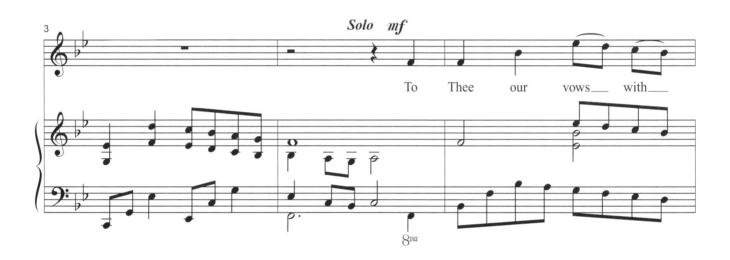

To Thee our vows with

sweet ac - cord, O Sav - ior now we say; We

© *2002 by SoundForth®, Greenville, SC 29614. All rights reserved. Printed in the U.S.A.*
Duplication in any form prohibited without written permission from the publisher.

Only Trust Him

John H. Stockton

James W. Koerts

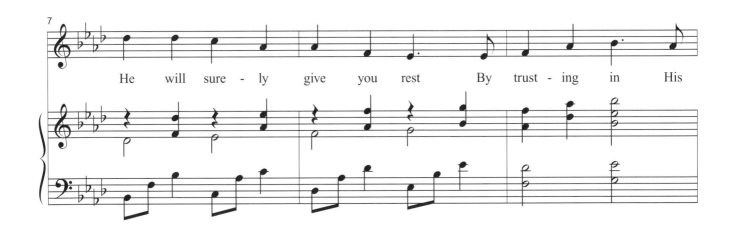

© 2002 by SoundForth®, Greenville, SC 29614. All rights reserved. Printed in the U.S.A.
Duplication in any form prohibited without written permission from the publisher.

Word.

For Je - sus shed His pre - cious blood, Rich

bless - ings to be - stow; Plunge

now in - to that crim - son___ flood That

for Taigen and Crystal

Savior, Like a Shepherd Lead Us

Dorothy A. Thrupp

Sandra H. Achterberg

© 2002 by SoundForth®, Greenville, SC 29614. All rights reserved. Printed in the U.S.A.
Duplication in any form prohibited without written permission from the publisher.

Do You Know Jesus?

Diane L. Parsons Bugg

Diane L. Parsons Bugg

© 2002 by SoundForth®, Greenville, SC 29614. All rights reserved. Printed in the U.S.A.
Duplication in any form prohibited without written permission from the publisher.

arms_____ are o-pen wide. He will give_____ you strength and com - fort. He will draw_____ you to His side. Do you know the Sav - ior of the world?_____ Do you know Je - sus,_____ God's on - ly

Breathe on Me, Breath of God

Edwin Hatch

Robert Jackson
Arranged by Abby Banks

© *2002 by SoundForth®, Greenville, SC 29614. All rights reserved. Printed in the U.S.A.*
Duplication in any form prohibited without written permission from the publisher.

Breathe on me, Breath of God,

So shall I nev - er die,

But live with Thee the

This One Thing

Karen Kuehmann
Based on Philippians 3:8-21

Dan Forrest Jr.

*An orchestral accompaniment CD is available for this song. Please call 1-800-258-7288.

© 2002 by SoundForth®, Greenville, SC 29614. All rights reserved. Printed in the U.S.A.
Duplication in any form prohibited without written permission from the publisher.

Christ has made us new._____ To share His pow'r and suf - f'ring, to die and then a - rise, As we seek to reach the goal, this one thing we do: We for - get the things be - hind us, and press on - ward to the prize, for as cit - i - zens of

heav - en liv - ing here,_____ We do ea - ger - ly a-

wait Him, Je - sus Christ who is our life; We press

on - ward 'til our Sav - ior shall ap - pear._____

poco accel.

Let us run the race with pa - tience, for we

77 know not when He will change us to His

80 glo - ry, when He comes a - gain. *rit.*

83 *f* *a tempo* We for - get the things be - hind us and press

86 on - ward to the prize, for as cit - i - zens of

heav - en liv - ing here, We do ea - ger - ly a-

wait Him, Je - sus Christ, who is our life; We press

on - ward 'til our Sav - ior shall ap - pear.____ We press

on - ward 'til our Sav - ior shall ap - pear.____

Jesus, I Am Resting, Resting

(Trombone obbligato)

Jean S. Pigott

Ruth Coleman

© 2002 by SoundForth®, Greenville, SC 29614. All rights reserved. Printed in the U.S.A.
Duplication in any form prohibited without written permission from the publisher.

NOTE: Permission to photocopy this instrumental part for your trombonist is granted without charge.

Complete in Thee

(Flute I obbligato)

Aaron R. Wolfe
Refrain, James M. Gray

Talmadge J. Bittikofer
Arranged by Alexander Kruchkov

© 2002 by SoundForth®, Greenville, SC 29614. All rights reserved. Printed in the U.S.A.
Duplication in any form prohibited without written permission from the publisher.

NOTE: Permission to photocopy this instrumental part for your flutist is granted without charge.

Complete in Thee

(Flute II obbligato)

Aaron R. Wolfe
Refrain, James M. Gray

Talmadge J. Bittikofer
Arranged by Alexander Kruchkov

© 2002 by SoundForth®, Greenville, SC 29614. All rights reserved. Printed in the U.S.A.
Duplication in any form prohibited without written permission from the publisher.

NOTE: Permission to photocopy this instrumental part for your flutist is granted without charge.

Index